It's another Quality Book from CGP

This book is for anyone doing GCSE Physical Education.

It contains lots of tricky questions designed
to make you sweat — because that's the only
way you'll get any better.

It's also got some daft bits in to try and make
the whole experience at least vaguely
entertaining for you.

What CGP is all about

Our sole aim here at CGP is to produce the highest quality
books — carefully written, immaculately presented and
dangerously close to being funny.

Then we work our socks off to get them out to you
— at the cheapest possible prices.

Contents

Published by Coordination Group Publications, Ltd.

ISBN: 1-84146-708-1

Groovy website: www.cgpbooks.co.uk

Jolly bits of clipart from CorelDRAW

Printed by Elanders Hindson, Newcastle upon Tyne.

Text, design, layout and original illustrations © Coordination Group Publications Ltd. 2002

Contributors:
Donella Crawford, Chris Dennett, James Wallis

Proofreading:
Angela Ryder, Charley Darbishire, Tim Major

Bones

Q1 How many bones are there in the human body? ....

Q2 The skeleton has five functions. Write in below what they are.

a) S....................   d) M....................

b) S....................   e) Making B................... C....................

c) P....................

Q3 There are four different types of bones.
List below what they are and give an example for each type.

a) L...................................   Example ....

b) S...................................   Example ....

c) F...................................   Example ....

d) I...................................   Example ....

Q4 Write down the technical name for each of the following bones.

a) Lower jaw   ....

b) Collarbone   ....

c) Shoulder Blade   ....

d) Skull   ....

e) Kneecap   ....

f) Breastbone   ....

Q5 Using words from the grey box below, complete the following sentences.

> shell, red blood cells, white blood cells, periosteum, jelly, ossification, maturity, cartilage, fat, sponge, red marrow, yellow marrow, blue marrow

All bones start as .... Over time they turn to bone through the process of .... The tough outer layer of the bone is called the .... and at each end of the bone there is a layer of .... The spongy part of the bone contains .... where .... are made. The marrow cavity contains .... where .... are formed.

Joints

Q1   Draw lines to match up the correct area of the vertebral column to the correct name.
The numbers in brackets on the diagram give the number of vertebrae in each section.

Coccyx

Thoracic vertebrae

Sacrum

Lumbar vertebrae

Cervical vertebrae

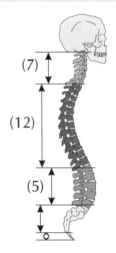

(7)

(12)

(5)

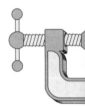

Q2   There are three types of connective tissue.   Write in below the job that each type does.

a)   Tendons attach .... to .... (or to other ....)

b)   Ligaments attach .... to ....

c)   Cartilage forms a .... between ....

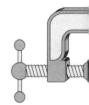

Q3   The three different types of joints allow different types of movement.
Complete the table below using words from the box.

> Slightly moveable, vertebrae, a little, shoulder,
> fixed, none, freely movable, skull, a lot

Technical name	Common name	Amount of movement	Example
Fibrous			
Cartilaginous			
Synovial			

__Joints__

Q1 Different joints allow different types of movement. Give an explanation of the different types of movement and give a sporting example of each one.

	Movement	Explanation	Example
a)	Extension		
b)	Flexion		
c)	Adduction		
d)	Abduction		
e)	Rotation		

Q2 Below is a list of the five different types of joints. Identify the type(s) of movement allowed by each joint — use the technical names.

a) Ball and Socket ....

b) Hinge ....

c) Pivot ....

d) Condyloid ....

e) Gliding ....

Q3 Write in below the type of joint for each example given.

a) Shoulder ....

b) Elbow ....

c) Atlas/Axis joint (Neck) ....

d) Hip ....

e) Between Tarsals ....

f) Knee ....

g) Wrist ....

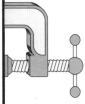

Muscles

Q1 Use the list of muscles below to label the diagram.

gastrocnemius, biceps, latissimus dorsi, abdominals, deltoids, gluteals,
quadriceps, hamstrings, triceps, trapezius, pectorals

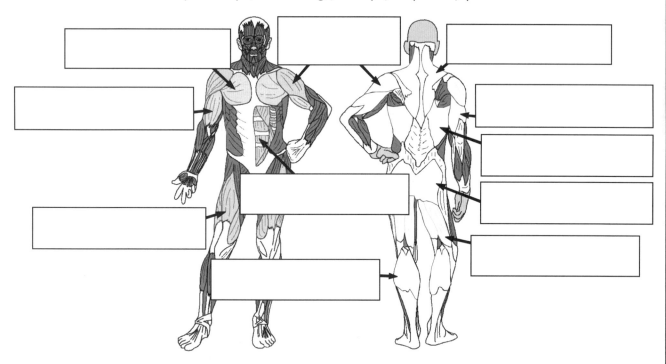

Q2 There are three different types of muscle in the body. Use a rule to
draw lines that match up the descriptions to the correct muscle type.

a) Cardiac   i) Attached to the skeleton to make movement. Under our conscious control.

b) Involuntary   ii) Found only in the heart. Work continuously without our conscious control.

c) Voluntary   iii) Found around internal organs. Work without our conscious control.

Q3 Complete the sentences below using words from the box.

Contract, more, different, string, relax, nervous system, fibres, similar, impulse, less.

Muscles are made up of .... Everyone has a .... number of

muscle fibres, but some have more of one type than the other.

A muscle will .... when it receives an ....

Fitter people have .... muscle fibres ready to be used. The nerve

impulses and the muscles are coordinated by the ....

Muscles

Q1   Muscles are attached to two bones by tendons. Complete the sentences below to identify which is the origin and which is the insertion of a muscle.

a) The origin attaches the muscle to the .... bone

b) The insertion attaches the muscle to the .... bone.

Q2   Complete the sentences below using words from the box.

> pairs, push, pull, biceps, antagonistic, synergist, triceps, contracts, relaxes, threes, prime mover, agonist, lift, antagonist, worker, lazy

Muscles always work in .... because they can only .... and not

.... These pairs are known as .... muscles. For movement to

occur, one muscle shortens (.....................), whilst the other muscle lengthens

(.....................). The muscle that contracts is known as the .... or

.... muscle. The muscle that relaxes is known as the .... muscle.

Muscles which hold the bone in place are known as .... muscles.

Q3   Draw straight lines to match the condition to the causes.

a) Muscle Fatigue

b) Muscle Atrophy

c) Cramp

d) Muscle Tone

i) Caused by lack of exercise

ii) Caused by lack of oxygen or overuse

iii) Caused by tension in the muscle

iv) Caused by a sudden contraction of muscle that won't relax

Jack mused on what to do with the human skins.

Q4   Outline the major differences in muscle length between an isometric and isotonic contraction.

....

....

Q5   Complete the table below to explain what happens as the elbow bends and straightens. Use these words: contracts/relaxes/biceps/triceps. (You can use each word more than once.)

Movement phase	Biceps	Triceps	Prime Mover	Antagonist
Elbow bends				
Elbow straightens				

The Respiratory System

Q1   Complete the sentence below to explain what the respiratory system does.

The respiratory system supplies our body with .... We breathe air into our

.... and the oxygen is then transferred into our .... It is then carried

all around the body.

Q2   Put the following words into the correct order to show the pathway of air in through the respiratory system: bronchioles, nose or mouth, gas exchange, alveoli, bronchi, trachea.

1 ....   4 ....

2 ....   5 ....

3 ....   6 ....

Q3   Tick the correct answer in each of the following statements.

i)   Gaseous exchange takes place in the...

a) nasal cavity ☐   b) alveoli ☐   c) heart ☐

ii)   How many alveoli are there in the lungs?

a) none ☐   b) twenty-six ☐   c) millions ☐

iii) The haemoglobin in the red blood cells combine with oxygen to make...

a) oxyhaemoglobin ☐   b) haemo-oxygen ☐   c) carbon dioxide ☐

iv) The oxygen is carried around the body by red blood cells. However the blood also picks up the carbon dioxide and takes it back to the...

a) diaphragm ☐   b) lungs ☐   c) villi ☐

Q4   Write a few short sentences to describe the difference between the air we breathe in and the air we breathe out.

....

....

....

....

The Respiratory System

Q1   Complete the sentences below to explain what happens when we breathe in and breathe out.

Breathing in is known as .... The diaphragm and intercostal muscles

........................, increasing the capacity of the chest .... Because of the

difference in air pressure, air is pushed into the .... Breathing out is known

as .... The diaphragm and intercostal muscles...................., making the

chest cavity .... This squeezes the lungs and air is forced ....

Q2   Draw straight lines to match the definitions with the correct lung capacity.

a) Tidal volume

b) Inspiratory Capacity

c) Expiratory Reserve Volume

d) Vital Capacity

e) Residual Volume

i)   The maximum amount of air you can breathe in or out in one breath

ii)   The amount of air left in the lungs after you have breathed out as much as you possibly can

iii) The actual amount of air breathed in (or out) in one breath

iv)   The amount of air you can forcibly breathe out after breathing out normally

v)   The maximum amount of air you can breathe in after breathing out.

Q3   List three immediate effects on the respiratory system caused by exercise.

1 ....

2 ....

3 ....

Q4   Write down a definition of VO_2 Max and explain how you can improve it.

Definition: ....

....

How to improve it: ....

....

Circulation

Q1   List three main functions of the circulatory system.

1 ....

2 ....

3 ....

Q2   Use only the words **to, from, pulmonary** and **systemic** to complete the following sentences.

The .... circuit carries blood .... the heart ....
the lungs and back .... the heart.

The .... circuit carries blood .... the heart ....
the rest of the body and back .... the heart.

Q3   Write a concise definition for each of the following terms.

a) Cardiac Output ....

b) Stroke Volume ....

c) Heart Rate ....

Q4   When blood pressure is measured it gives two readings. What do these two readings mean?

Systolic Pressure ....

Diastolic Pressure ....

Q5   List the following words in the correct order to show the pathway of blood around the body through the double circulatory pump. (Two of them have been done for you.)

Left atrium, right atrium, left ventricle, right ventricle, tricuspid valve, bicuspid valve, semi-lunar valve, aorta, rest of body, vena cava, pulmonary artery, lungs, pulmonary vein

1 Vena cava   8 Pulmonary vein

2 ....   9 ....

3 ....   10 ....

4 ....   11 ....

5 ....   12 ....

6 ....   13 ....

7 ....

Circulation

Q1   List three physiological factors and one psychological factor that may affect blood pressure.

Physiological 1 ....   Psychological   4 ....

2 ....

3 ....

Q2   List three risks of long term high blood pressure and describe the symptoms of each.

1   Risk: ....

Symptoms: ....

2   Risk: ....

Symptoms: ....

3   Risk: ....

Symptoms: ....

Q3   Using words from the box, complete the sentences below.

> thick, arterioles, bolts, food, veins, heart, venules, arteries, oxygen, stringy, locks, thinner, oxygenated, deoxygenated, thin, elastic, thicker, pressure, valves, waste, water

.... carry .... blood away from the heart. Their walls are thick,

strong and .... to cope with the pressure. .... are very small

arteries. .... carry .... blood back to the heart. Their walls are

much .... as blood .... is much lower in them. To stop blood

flowing in the wrong direction, veins have .... Smaller veins are called

.... Capillaries carry .... and .... to all the tissues and

also remove .... They are very small and have very .... walls.

Q4   Draw lines to match the main constituents of blood to their main function.

a) Red Blood Cells   i) Help the blood to clot

b) White Blood Cells   ii) Carries everything in the bloodstream

c) Platelets   iii) Fight against disease

d) Plasma   iv) Carry oxygen in haemoglobin

Health

Q1 Being healthy is not just about the absence of disease.
List the three components of health as defined by the World Heath Organisation.

1. P.. 2. M.. 3. S..

Q2 Put the following states of health in the correct column in the table.

a) Free from disease
b) Low levels of stress/anxiety
c) Injury free
d) Feel content
e) Have friends
f) Organs are healthy and working
g) Sufficient food and shelter
h) No mental illness
i) Feeling of worth

Physical well-being	Mental well-being	Social well-being

Q3 The acronym PLEASED is often used to remember the things that can affect your health. For each letter, state what it stands for and then explain how it can affect your health. I've done the first one for you, coz I'm nice like that.

P *ersonal hygiene*............ Affect on health *Helps to avoid disease through contamination.*...........

L............................ Affect on health ....
....

E............................ Affect on health ....
....

A............................ Affect on health ....
....

S............................ Affect on health ....
....

E............................ Affect on health ....
....

D............................ Affect on health ....
....

Fitness

Q1 Complete the definitions of General Fitness and Specific fitness below.

a) General fitness means you are fit for ....

b) Specific fitness means you are fit for ....

Q2 List the four S's that make up general fitness.

S....................   S....................   S....................   S....................

Q3 Explain why the following components are also important for general fitness.

a) Cardiovascular endurance ....

b) Muscular endurance ....

c) Good body composition ....

Q4 Define the following components of specific fitness.

a) Agility ....

b) Balance ....

c) Coordination ....

d) Explosive strength ....

e) Fast reactions ....

f) Good timing ....

Q5 List six factors that can affect fitness.   Hint: Think 'HIP DAD'

1 ....   4 ....

2 ....   5 ....

3 ....   6 ....

Q6 Write a few short sentences to explain the difference between cardiovascular fitness and muscular fitness, and why they are both important for people who play sport.

....

....

....

Exercise

Q1   Draw lines up to match the benefits of exercise on the right to the correct group on the left.

A) Physical Benefits

B) Mental Benefits

C) Social Benefits

i) Gives you challenge

ii) Improves teamwork

iii) Improves body shape

iv) Increases strength, endurance, flexibility and fitness

v) Helps relieve stress

vi) Make new friends

vii) Feel-good factor

viii) Increases life expectancy and reduces illness

ix) Improve image of yourself

Q2   When starting a training programme, it is important to consider the physical condition and the long-term goals of the person involved.

a)   List 3 examples of people who should see a doctor before starting a training programme

   i) ....

   ii) ....

   iii) ....

b)   Give three different examples of the types of fitness goals people might set themselves

   i) ....

   ii) ....

   iii) ....

Q3   When starting an exercise programme, list three safety guidelines that everyone should follow that will help avoid injury.

   1 ....

   2 ....

   3 ....

Q4   Some people could get fitter by simply changing their daily routine. Give two examples of changes that any of your friends (or their parents) could make to get more exercise each day.

   1 ....

   2 ....

The Effects of Exercise

Q1   Draw straight lines to match the following.

a) When you start to exercise, more oxygen is needed, so you start to breathe...

b) Your heart beats faster to circulate more blood, therefore arterioles widen to...

c) The blood supply is diverted away from organs to working muscles by blood vessels either...

d) The veins squeeze the blood back to the heart more quickly and the heart stretches....

i)   ...contracts stronger, pumping out more blood.

ii)   ...quicker and deeper.

iii) ...widening (vasodilation) or narrowing (vasoconstriction).

iv)   ...prevent blood pressure becoming too high.

Q2   List the three ways the body keeps the blood cool when exercising.

i)   ....

ii)   ....

iii) ....

Hello, is this demon fighting for beginners? I've heard it's awfully good exercise

Q3   Using words from the box, complete the sentences below to explain what happens in recovery.

oxygen debt, rises, oxygen, forty-eight, damaged, repaired, faster, fatter, fitter, lactic acid, lower, fitness, fat, intensity, long, fall, bank manager, glycogen, two

When you stop exercising, your heart rate begins to .... The fitter you

are, the .... it will fall. The time taken to recover fully from exercise

will depend upon the................................. of the exercise and the level of

.... of the person. .... stores are used up during

exercise and these can take up to .... hours to be replaced. Muscles

can also be damaged during exercise and they need time to be ....

A poisonous substance called .... builds up in the muscles during

exercise, and so lots of .... is needed to help flush this out.

This process is known as repaying the ....

The Effects of Exercise

Q1   Draw lines to match up the following pairs to explain the long-term benefits of training.

a)   The body makes more red blood cells, so...

b)   Arteries get bigger and more elasticated, so...

c)   More capillaries are formed, so...

d)   The heart gets bigger and stronger. So...

e)   After exercise, heart rate returns to...

i)   ...oxygen is delivered more efficiently.

ii)   ...stroke volume is increased.

iii) ...it can transport more oxygen.

iv) ...its resting level more quickly.

v)   ...blood pressure falls.

Q2   Fill in the blanks using words from the box below to explain the long-term effects of exercise on the respiratory system.

biceps, longer, chest cavity, less, rib size, gaseous exchange, capillaries, vital capacity, oxygen debt, diaphragm, more

The .... and intercostal muscles get stronger and increase the

.... This means you can take in .... air, increasing

.... More .... means that ....

can take place quicker and you can exercise for ....

Q3   List four physiological benefits of endurance training.

1 ....

2 ....

3 ....

4 ....

Q4   Complete the sentences below to give a clear definition of hypertrophy.

Hypertrophy is when the muscles ....

Tendons also become ....

Q5   List 2 ways in which a trained athlete deals better with lactic acid than an untrained athlete.

1.   ....

2.   ....

Diet and Nutrition

Q1   Write in below the three main components of food that provide energy.

1. P...........................   2. C...........................   3. F...........................

Q2   Complete the table below.

Food type	Main job	Found in	Recommended % in diet
Protein			
Simple carbohydrates			
Complex carbohydrates			
Saturated fats			
Monosaturated fats			
Polyunsaturated fats			

Q3   The following vitamins and minerals are needed to maintain a balanced diet. Write in below the main job that each does and give two examples of food types where each can be found.

Vitamin A: Main job: ....

              Found in: ....

Vitamin D   Main job: ....

              Found in: ....

Vitamin C   Main job: ....

              Found in: ....

Calcium   Main job: ....

              Found in: ....

Iron   Main job: ....

              Found in: ....

Iodine   Main job: ....

              Found in: ....

Q4   What is the major difference between fat-soluble vitamins A and D
      and water-soluble vitamin C? Hint : Think about storage and intake.

      ....

      ....

      ....

Diet and Nutrition

Q1   Fill in the blanks using words from the box below.

> sweets, good, digestive, vegetables, chocolate, uses, urine, sweat,
> kidneys, breathe, dehydrated, fruit, bad, respiratory, heart

Water is needed to help with many chemical reactions in the body. We lose water when

we ....,........................ or go to the toilet. If the water lost is not

replaced, we become .... and this has a .... effect on

performance. If we take in too much water, the .... will produce more

.... to get rid of it. Fibre is another important element of a balanced diet.

It is found in .... and .... and helps to keep the

.... system working properly.

Q2   Explain what is meant by a balanced diet.
      Hint: Mention the different food types and amount of intake.

      ....

      ....

      ....

Q3   Explain how and why the diet of a sprinter, a gymnast and a marathon runner would vary.

      ....

      ....

      ....

Q4   Fill in below some Do's and Don't's advice for an
      athlete on when to eat and drink in relation to activity.

      a)   Before an activity: DO ....

      b)   During an activity: DO ....

                                  DON'T ....

      c)   After activity: DO ....

                                  DON'T ....

Energy

Q1 Complete the following sentence.

The amount of energy needed by the body to just keep the heart beating and the body breathing is known as the B........................ M........................ R........................

Q2 List five things that you do most days that require more energy than the BMR.

1 ....
2 ....
3 ....
4 ....
5 ....

There's room for you on the second shelf, Susan. Right next to those hams.

Q3 Complete the following formulas by adding **gain**, **loss** or **remains constant**.

1. Energy input = energy output: weight ....
2. Energy input < energy output: weight ....
3. Energy input > energy output: weight ....

TIP:
> means "is greater than".
< means "is less than".

Q4 Energy requirements are determined by four main factors. For each category below, give an example of someone who would need a large intake and someone who would need a smaller intake of energy.

1. **Age:**

   Large intake ....

   Smaller intake ....

2. **Lifestyle:**

   Large intake ....

   Smaller intake ....

3. **Sports Players:**

   Large intake ....

   Smaller intake ....

4. **Size and Gender:**

   Large intake ....

   Smaller intake ....

Q5 Explain why exercising more is a far better way of losing weight than just dieting.

....
....
....

Endurance

Q1   Complete the following sentences using words from the box below.

> weights, slow, less, hypertrophy, more, fatigue, speed, fast

When muscle .... sets in, your muscles become tired and don't function

properly. Muscles with lots of .... twitch fibres will tire

.... quickly. Training with .... is a good way to

develop muscular endurance.

Q2   Draw lines to complete the sentences below.

a) When muscles work hard they need
    more oxygen, so...

i)   ...will return to resting rate
      quicker when exercise stops.

b) An efficient cardiovascular system will
    produce a slower heart rate and...

ii)   ...fifteen minutes within your
      aerobic training zone.

c) To improve cardiovascular fitness you
    must work for at least...

iii) ...breathing rate and heart rate
      both increase.

Q3   Complete the table below to show the differences between aerobic and
      anaerobic respiration. Use the following words / phrases / equations:

long,   lactic acid,   short/explosive,   not enough,

Glucose + O_2 → CO_2 + H_2O + energy,   Glucose → lactic acid + energy + CO_2 + sweat,

endurance,   short,   plenty

Respiration type	Amount of O_2 supplied	By-products	Time energy supplied for	Events using it	Formula
aerobic					
anaerobic					

Strength, Speed and Power

Q1 Fill in the table below with the correct types of
strength and sporting examples from the list below.

Static Strength, Explosive strength, Dynamic strength, High Jump, Arm wrestling, Cycling

Strength type	Definition	Sporting example
	to apply force repeatedly for a long time.	
	to apply force on an immovable object (muscle remains the same length).	
	to apply a lot of force for a very short amount of time	

Q2 List four sporting examples where it is important to have quick reactions.

1 ....

2 ....

3 ....

4 ....

Q3 Complete the following sentences using words from the box below.

strength, technique, more, size, weight, fast twitch, less, slow twitch, speed

Speed can be improved with training. However, people with more ....

fibres will be able to improve it .... than people with a lot of slow twitch

fibres. To improve speed you need to develop more .... and make sure

you use the correct .... A person's bone structure, ...

and muscle .... will determine how fast they can move.

Q4 Power is a combination of speed and strength. Give an example
for each of the following sports where power would be needed.

1. Gymnastics ....

2. Rugby ....

3. Sprinting ....

4. Javelin ....

*Franz lacked a bit of power
in the leg department.*

Flexibility

Q1 Flexibility is often referred to by other names.
Write in below **two** other common names for flexibility.

1. S.....................................

2. M.....................................

Q2 Write in reasons why flexibility helps with sporting performance.

1. Gives less injuries because ....

2. Provides better posture which means ....

3. It makes you more efficient because ....

Q3 For each body part below, name one sport that it would be beneficial
to have good flexibility in. Name a different sport for each one.

a) Back ....

b) Hip ....

c) Knee/ankle ....

d) Shoulder/elbow ....

Q4 Complete the DO's and DON'Ts advice for stretching using the pictures as clues.

a) DO ....

....

b) DON'T ....

....

c) DON'T ....

....

Q5 Write a few short sentences to highlight the difference
between active stretching and passive stretching.

Hint: Think about who makes the stretch.

....

....

....

Age and Gender

Q1   Draw straight lines to match up the statements to the correct effect of age.
The numbers in the brackets tell you how many statements match up to each box.

1. Old bones and muscles are more susceptible to this.

2. You can still improve it easily until your early 30s.

3. After the age of 30 you start to lose it!

4. The older you get, the slower this gets!

5. This is at your best during your teens.

6. Old people tend to suffer more of this.

a. Strength (3)

b. Injury/disease (3)

c. Flexibility (2)

d. Oxygen capacity (1)

e. Reaction time (1)

f. Experience (1)

7. Older people tend to have more.

8. It takes older people longer to recover from this.

9. Your reach your maximum about 20 yrs old

10. This decreases as you get older.

11. After 30, protein levels begin to fall, so you have less of this.

Q2   List two sports where you think being older (over 40) is a disadvantage, and two sports where you think it makes very little difference.

Disadvantage in .... and ....

Very little difference in .... and ....

Q3   Complete the sentences below using only the following words: more, less, higher, lower, bigger, earlier, later. (Some words may be used more than once and some not at all.)

Men have .... muscles than women because they have

.... levels of testosterone. Women have a ....

percentage of body fat than men and tend to be .... flexible.

However, women tend to reach physical maturity .... than men.

Q4   Write in below another major biological factor that may influence a woman's performance that definitely does not affect men.

....

Somatotype

Q1 List below the three extreme body types.

....

....

....

Q2 Complete the names of the three body types (in the white boxes) and use the characteristics from the box below to complete the descriptions of each one.

wide, narrow, fat, thin, muscle

a) En............................. : .... hips, ... shoulders.

A lot of .... on body. .... ankles and wrists.

b) Me............................. : .... shoulders, ... hips

A lot of .... on body. Not much .... on body.

c) Ec............................. : .... shoulders, hips and chest.

Not much .... or .... on body. ....

arms, legs and face.

Q3 Body shape is described by three numbers (End:Meso:Ecto). Scores from six different people are written below. Write in which somatotype each person is nearest to.

a) 711.............................

b) 171.............................

c) 117.............................

d) 242.............................

e) 622.............................

f) 444.............................

No way are you a mesomorph crab-boy!

Q4 For each body type, name two sports that they would be well suited to.

a) Endomorph: .... and ....

b) Mesomorph: .... and ....

c) Ectomorph: .... and ....

Sport and Personality

Q1 Different personality types favour different demands from sport.
Write each demand in the correct personality box.

concentration, simple skills, excitement, precision, intricate skills, arousal, team involvement, self-motivation, less thinking, less pain, individual performance, calm, speed, more pain, less arousal, less concentration, activity, thinking

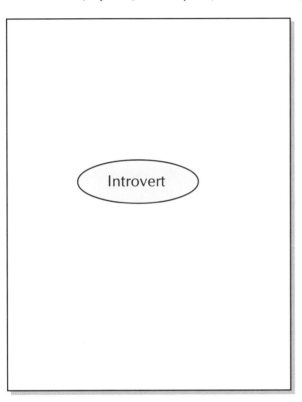

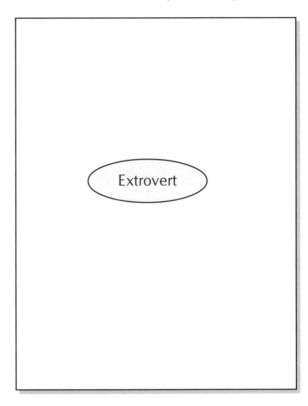

Q2 List three sports that an extreme introvert would normally be attracted to, and three sports that an extreme extrovert would normally be attracted to.

Introvert

1...

2...

3...

Extrovert

1...

2...

3...

Q3 Write in below an explanation of assertion (sometimes called good aggression) and bad aggression, giving a sporting example for each.

Assertion ....

Example ....

Bad aggression ....

Example ....

Hygiene

Q1   Complete the sentences below to give some good advice on hygiene.

   a) Shower or bath regularly to avoid .... , ... & ....

   b) Clean your teeth at least twice a day to avoid .... , ... and
       ....

   c) Change your clothes regularly to avoid ....

Q2   Draw lines to connect the foot problems in the middle to the correct
      descriptions on the left and to the correct treatments on the right.

i) Inflammation of joint	a) Blister	A) Surgery
ii) Caused by rubbing	b) Bunion	B) Corn plasters
iii) Hard pads of skin	c) Corn	C) Cover and keep clean

Q3   Complete the table below.

Infection	What is it?	How do you get it?	Treatment
Athlete's Foot			
Verruca			

Drugs

Q1   Name two drugs that many sportspeople take which are legal but still harmful.

a) T ....

b) A ....

Q2   Complete the sentences below.

Alcohol affects your co .... , sp .... and ju ....

It also slows down your re .... and makes your muscles t .... quicker. Long term effects of alcohol include damage to your l .... ,

k .... , h .... , m .... , b .... ,

d .... system and i .... system.

Smoking makes you short of b .... , causes irritations in the n ....,

t .... , and chest and increases the risk of h ....

d .... , l .... c .... and b ....

Q3   There are 5 main groups of performance enhancing drugs banned by the IOC. For a) to e) below, name each group of drugs and write down its benefits and side effects.

a) S ....

Benefit to performer ....

Side effects ....

b) N .... A ....

Benefit to performer ....

Side effects ....

c) A .... A .... (S ....)

Benefit to performer ....

Side effects ....

d) P .... H ....

Benefit to performer ....

Side effects ....

e) D ....

Benefit to performer ....

Side effects ....

Drugs

Q1 The IOC has also restricted the use of five other groups of drugs.
Write in the spaces below what they are and what they do.

a) B............................ B............................

Effect: ....

b) C............................ Effect: ....

c) A............................ Effect: ....

d) L............................ A............................

Effect: ....

e) M............................ Effect: ....

Q2 Urine sampling is the most common form of testing an athlete for drugs.
Complete the sentences below to explain the process.

Athletes can be tested for .... at .... time; they do not have

to be in a competition. When a urine sample is taken, it is divided into ....

bottles to give an A and a B sample. If .... are found in sample A, then the

B sample is tested to .... - .... the result. If the athlete is found

.... of taking drugs , they will be .... from competing.

.... to give a sample carries the same penalties as failing a drugs test. If

anyone is found to have .... with the sample after it has been given, this

also carries serious penalties.

Q3 Blood doping is an illegal but difficult to trace method of enhancing performance.
In the space below, write in the three main steps in the process.

Step 1: Red blood cells ....

Step 2: The body ....

Step 3: Before a competition ....

Q4 How can athletes gain an increase in red blood cells legally?

....

Q5 List four possible harmful effects of blood doping.

a) .... c) ....

b) .... d) ....

Other Things that Affect Performance

Q1   For each of the medical conditions below, write in the effect they can have on the body.

a) Cold or flu: Effect on body ....

b) Asthma: Effect on body ....

c) Hay fever: Effect on body ....

d) Anaemia: Effect on body ....

Q2   Put the following conditions in the table to match the effects.

a) Staleness   b) Fatigue   c) Lack of sleep   d) Menstrual cycle

Condition	Effects
	i) Women can perform better at certain times.
	ii) If you don't give yourself enough time to recover your performance will suffer from this.
	iii) Lose strength and concentration more quickly.
	iv) If you over train and don't give yourself enough breaks you can suffer from this.

Q3   Name the abilities below that can affect performance.

a) A.............................: the ability to change direction quickly.

b) B.............................: the ability to hold a position.

c) C.............................: the ability to move a number of body parts smoothly and precisely.

Q4   There are five other factors that are difficult to change which can also affect performance. In the spaces below, explain how some performers may benefit more than others from the following factors.

(HINT: For some of the answers think about the money)

a) Sharp senses: ....

b) Equipment: ....

c) Technology: ....

d) Physical Ability: ....

e) Altitude: ....

Training Sessions

Q1 Complete the sentences below, using words from the box to fill in the blanks.

> stretching   warm up   size   temperature   heart
> movement   injury   shower   focused   muscles

Before taking part in any physical exercise, everyone should ....

By increasing the .... of the body and increasing blood flow to the

.... , the body becomes better prepared for exercise. ....

the muscles not only increases the range of .... , it also means the athlete is

less likely to get a muscle .... As well as the body being physically

prepared, a good warm up also helps the mind to become more ....

Q2 After physical exercise, a 'cool down' should be performed.
Tick the boxes below that indicate reasons why we cool down.

☐ a) Help repay the oxygen debt   ☐ e) Get rid of unused energy

☐ b) Prevent blood pooling   ☐ f) To build muscle

☐ c) To increase lung capacity   ☐ g) To stop stiffness the next day

☐ d) Help remove lactic acid and   ☐ h) Help return body systems to normal
   other waste products

Q3 Each one of the following are important elements of a training session.
For each one, write down why they are important.

a) Warm up ....

....

b) Variety ....

....

c) Regular testing and reviewing ....

....

Q4 SPOR is the acronym used to help remind you of the four principles of training.
Write down the principle each letter stands for and explain what is meant by each term.

S................................. Meaning: ....

P................................. Meaning: ....

O................................. Meaning: ....

R................................. Meaning: ....

Training Sessions

Q1 When planning a training programme, list five points you would need to consider about the person who the training programme is for.

a) ....

b) ....

c) ....

d) ....

e) ....

SOLDIER! Camouflage training
is useless if you forget the basics.

Q2 There are four stages to training for competition. Draw straight lines to match each stage to the type of training involved in each stage.

a) Out of season preparation	i) Maintaining fitness and ensuring sufficient rest. "Peak" at the right time
b) Pre-season preparation	ii) Recovery and relaxation
c) Competition	iii) High carbohydrate diet, general strength and endurance training
d) Recuperation	iv) All round general fitness training. Skills training. Strength training

Q3 The FITT principle should be applied to all training programmes. Write in below what each letter stands for and an explanation of what it means.

a) F .... How .... you train

b) I .... How .... you train

c) T .... How .... you train

d) T .... What .... of training

Q4 The weather can greatly affect training programmes. Write down the effect that weather can have and explain how some athletes manage to beat the weather.

....

....

....

....

Training Methods

Q1 Draw straight lines to match the example to the correct form of strength.

a) Explosive strength

b) Static strength

c) Dynamic strength

i) moving a heavy object

ii) throwing a discus

iii) holding up a heavy object

Q2 Complete the table below using the following phrases.

Strengthens muscle throughout range of movement,   develops static strength,

blood flow to muscles is reduced during exercise,   adaptable for most sports,

muscles can develop soreness from stress,   no good for heart problems,

cheap/quick/do it anywhere.

Type of training	Advantages	Disadvantages
Isometric		
Isotonic		

Q3 List three methods that could be used in training to put more psychological pressure on the player.

a) ....

b) ....

c) ....

Q4 Identify one advantage and one disadvantage of this style of pressure training.

a) Advantage ....

....

b) Disadvantage ....

....

Training Methods

Q1 Draw lines to match the correct definitions to the type of training.

a) Circuit Training

b) Continuous Training

c) Fartlek Training

d) Interval Training

i) Fixed patterns of exercises, involving "reps" and "sets".

ii) Stations with different exercises to work different muscle groups.

iii) Training at a steady rate for at least an hour.

iv) "Speed play" – continuous exercise involving a variety of speeds.

Q2 Write down two advantages and two disadvantages of using the circuit training method for a group of people.

....

....

....

....

Q3 Complete the table below using the following sentences:

difficult to tell if person is trying,   can be really boring,

uses up body fat,   doesn't improve speed,

good for games that constantly change pace,   easy to miss out the hard bits,

easy to see when person isn't trying,   can be hard to stay motivated,

little or no equipment needed,   easily adapted to suit person's needs.

Type of Training	Advantages	Disadvantages
Continuous		
Fartlek		
Interval		

Q4 For each type of training, write in below how you would introduce the principle of overload.

a) Circuit Training: ....

b) Continuous Training: ....

c) Fartlek Training: ....

d) Interval Training: ....

Aerobic Fitness Testing

Q1 Complete the following sentences to describe someone with a high level of aerobic fitness compared to someone of average fitness.

i) Their .... heart rate will be ....

ii) They will be able to exercise for .... without feeling tired.

iii) They make more efficient use of ....

Q2 Fill in the blanks using some words from the box below.

> carrot, little finger, four, radial, thumb, pulse points, one minute
> six, heart rate, carotid, thirty seconds, radial, first two fingers, two

To measure your pulse, put your .... on one of the two

.... The point on your neck allows you to feel the pulse

in the .... artery. The point on your wrist allows you to feel

the pulse in the .... artery. You need to count the number of

beats in fifteen seconds and then multiply by ....

This will give you your .... which is how many times your

heart beats in ....

Q3 Name three tests that help to measure your aerobic fitness.

1 ....

2 .... (Cooper Test)

3 .... (The Bleep Test)

Q4 Explain in detail how the multistage fitness test is performed.
Hint : Make sure you explain when it's time to stop.

....

....

....

....

Fitness Testing

Q1 Draw lines to match up the test description to the correct component of fitness.

a) Muscular Endurance

b) Balance

c) Agility

d) Speed

e) Strength

i) A timed course with lots of changes of direction

ii) Dynamometer

iii) Number of sit-ups

iv) Stork stand

v) Timed sprint

Q2 Complete the sentences below.

The stork stand test is used to test ....

Stand on your .... and place your other foot on the side of your knee.

Put your hands on your .... and close your eyes. Start timing.

Stop timing when you .... your eyes or .... your hands or feet.

Breaker breaker
Come in Mr. Hare
I've got a smokey
on my tail

Q3 List three rules you should follow during the shoulder lift test.

1 Keep your hands .... apart.

2 Lift the stick with .... arms.

3 Keep your .... on the floor.

Q4 Describe below how to perform the sit and reach test.

....
....
....
....

Sporting Injuries

Q1 Name two common overuse injuries by filling in the missing letters.

a) T............................ e............................

b) S............................ s............................

Q2 One cause of overuse injuries is lack of rest. Name three others.

1 ....

2 ....

3 ....

Q3 For the following acute injuries, give a sporting example of how they might occur.

1. Colliding with an opponent or object   E.g...

2. Being hit by something   E.g...

3. Falling from a height   E.g...

4. Falling at speed   E.g...

Q4 List below two safety rules that should be followed to avoid injury before, during and after activity.

Before activity:

a) ....

b) ....

During Activity:

c) ....

d) ....

After Activity

e) ....

f) ....

Sporting Injuries

Q1   Beside each soft tissue injury, write in whether it
     is classed as an OPEN injury or a CLOSED injury.

     i) Sprain   ....

     ii) Cut   ....

     iii) Strain   ....

     iv) Bruise   ....

     v) Dislocation   ....

     vi) Graze   ....

WE HAVE A DUMPTY DOWN
REPEAT, WE HAVE A DUMPTY DOWN

Q2   Fill in the blank using words from the box below. I've done one for you.

> cartilage, muscle, tendon, ligament, sprain, strain,
> stress, overstretching, overeating, twisting, tissue

When you pull a muscle or tendon, it is known as a .... It is caused by

.... and leads to tears in the .... When you stretch or

tear a .... *ligament* ...., it is known as a .... It is often caused by

.... the joint badly. .... can also be damaged by

twisting badly.

Q3   Write true or false for each of the following statements.

     i)   A fracture is a cracked or broken bone   ....

     ii) All bone injuries are closed injuries   ....

     iii) Damaged blood vessels cause bruising and swelling   ....

     iv) A stress fracture is caused by continuous stress   ....

     v)   A stress fracture is an acute injury   ....

     vi) A sprain is a soft tissue injury   ....

Q4   Outline the difference between an open fracture and a closed fracture.
     HINT: Think gory details.

     ....

     ....

     ....

     ....

Injury — Types and Treatment

Q1   Say whether the symptoms and treatments below are concerned with
A: **HYPO**THERMIA or B: **HYPER**THERMIA. Tick the correct box after each one.

A ☐ B ☐   i)   Body temperature too high   A ☐ B ☐   v)   Rigid muscles

A ☐ B ☐   ii) Irregular heartbeat   A ☐ B ☐   vi) Clammy skin

A ☐ B ☐   iii) Body temperature too low   A ☐ B ☐   vii) Cool place and lots of fluid

A ☐ B ☐   iv) Weak pulse   A ☐ B ☐   viii) Wrap in blanket and hot drink

Q2   Put the following conditions and treatments into the correct part of the table.

Conditions: cramp, winding, shock, concussion, stitch

Treatments: deep breaths, stretch and massage, recovery position and ambulance
lean forward and rub affected area, (if conscious) keep an eye on for 24hrs

	Description	Condition	Treatment
a)	Disorientated after bump on head		
b)	Painful, involuntary contraction of muscle		
c)	Sharp pain in side or abdomen		
d)	Pale, clammy skin, weak breathing, feeling faint		
e)	Difficulty in breathing after blow to stomach		

Q3   The RICE method is often used to treat soft tissue injuries.
Fill in below what each letter stands for.

i) R ....   ii) I ....   iii) C ....   iv) E ....

Q4   Tick the correct boxes to identify whether the following statements are true or false.

True   False

☐ ☐   a) Hyperthermia is caused by eating too many E numbers.

☐ ☐   b) A rugby player was unconscious for three seconds after a bang of heads.
He is okay to play on.

☐ ☐   c) Cramp is caused by lack of blood flow to the muscle.

☐ ☐   d) The RICE method should be used on a fracture.

Injury — Types and Treatment

Q1 DRABC (or Dr. Abc) is the first aid treatment. Write below what each letter stands for.

D............................ R............................

A............................ B............................ C............................

Q2 List four things you should do when checking the airway is clear.

a) ....

b) ....

c) ....

d) ....

Q3 Draw lines to match the correct responses to the following conditions.

a) Casualty is breathing

b) There is a pulse but the casualty is not breathing

c) There is no pulse

i) Check airway, give mouth to mouth

ii) Check airway, give mouth to mouth and cardiac massage

iii) Put in recovery position

Q4 Fill in the blanks from the box below.

> rise, fall, nose, close, help, breath, into, themselves, out of, mouth, tongue, oxygen, carbon dioxide, pinch, punch

When you give mouth to mouth, you are forcing .... into the casualty's

lungs. It is important to get a good seal on all escape routes for this oxygen so you need to

.... the casualty's .... and make sure your

.... makes a seal over their .... If the oxygen is getting

in, you should be able to see their chest .... as you breathe

.... them and .... as you pull away to take another

.... You should continue to breathe for the casualty until either they start

to breathe for .... or .... arrives.

Q5 Should full mouth-to-mouth or cardiac massage be practised on someone who is well?

Yes or no? ....

Skills

Q1   Complete the following sentence using words from the box below.

> efficiency, minimum, natural,
> result, learned, maximum, energy

Skill is the .... ability to bring about the .... you want,

with .... certainty and ....

Q2   List three basic action skills that most of us learn from an early age.

i)   R...........................

ii)   J...........................

iii) T...........................

Q3   Write in below the two 'C's that complex skills require more of than basic skills.

a)   C...........................

b)   C...........................

Q4   Write in beside each skill whether it is a more 'open' or a more 'closed' skill.

i) Basketball free throw   ....

ii) Pass in rugby   ....

iii) Handstand   ....

iv) Catching a rounders ball   ....

v) Throwing a shot putt   ....

Q5   Put the following parts of information processing into the correct order.

a) Decision Making   ....

b) Feedback   ....

c) Output   ....

d) Input   ....

Skills

Q1   List the three main senses that are used to input information.

a)   S...............................

b)   H...............................

c)   T...............................

Q2   Complete the sentences using words from the box below.

> memory, foot, slowly, heart, brain, perception,
> outcomes, being picky, respond, quickly
> selective attention, channel capacity, size

The senses send all the input information to the ....

It then interprets the information (..............................) and keeps all the important

information and disregards irrelevant stuff.

This is known as ....

The brain searches the .... to see if it has stored any similar situations,

and depending on past .... , it decides how best to ....

The brain only has a limited .... which means it can only

process a certain amount of information at any time. However, this all happens very

.... , especially with experienced players.

Q3   Use the jumbled boxes and arrows to draw a diagram on
the right to show how information processing works.

Feedback

Decision making

Input

Perception

Output

Memory

Motivation and Mental Preparation

Q1   Write in below what the two forms of motivation are.

a) I .... : from inside.

b) E .... : rewards for success.

Q2   From the graph below, indicate what level of arousal competitors A, B and C are at and suggest reasons for their state of arousal.

A: Arousal level is ....

Possible reason: ....

B: Arousal level is ....

Possible reason: ....

C: Arousal level is ....

Possible reason: ....

Performance / *Better*

B

C

A

Low (bored)   High (anxious)

Arousal Level

Q3   List three common extrinsic motivators.

i)   M...............................   ii)   T............................... or M...............................

iii) P...............................

Q4   Performers need to set goals that meet 7 criteria.   Write out these criteria below.

i)   S...............................

ii) M...............................

iii) A...............................

iv) R...............................

v)   T...............................

vi) E...............................

vii) R...............................

TIP: The word SMARTER gives you the first letter of each criterion.

Any ideas about what the cause of death might have been?

Q5   Give an example of one short-term goal and one long-term goal in any sport.

Sport...............................   Short-term goal ....

Long-term goal ....

Leisure and Recreation

Q1   Fill in the blanks to give a definition of leisure.

Leisure is .... time when you can do what you .... and not

things that .... to be done. A lot of people take part in ....

during their leisure time.

Q2   Draw lines to match the definitions to the correct title.

i) Very competitive

ii) Not too competitive

a) Sport

iii) Can make up own rules

iv) Follow governing body rules

b) Recreation

v) Aim is to win

vi) Aim is to enjoy

Q3   List three reasons why leisure time has increased over the last decade.

a) ....

b) ....

c) ....

Q4   Young sportspeople often rely on family for two very important needs of sport.
List them below and explain why they are needed.

a) M...........................

Needed for   ....

b) T...........................

Needed to   ....

Q5   Write in below the difference that having a group of friends with a
positive attitude to sport and having a group of friends with a
negative attitude to sport may have on your participation in sport.

a) Positive attitude ....

b) Negative attitude ....

Participation in Sport

Q1 Explain how schools are important in promoting participation in sport.

....

....

....

Q2 There are 9 other key areas that affect the type of sport people participate in. The clue
    SPAMFACET gives you the first letter of each of these areas. Use the picture clues to
    identify what each letter stands for. Then explain how each one affects sports participation.

a) S..................... :

....

b) P..................... :

....

c) A..................... :

....

d) M..................... :

....

e) F..................... :

....

f) A cceptability......... :

....

g) C........................ / .... :

....

h) E..................... :

....

i) T..................... :

....

Women in Sport

Q1 Complete the sentences using words from the box below.

> dogs, revealed, covered, men, less, more, women, uncomfortable,
> attractive, injuring, household, garden, unattractive, better

In the past sport was seen to be for .... only. It was thought that

women involved in sport were .... and risked ....

themselves. If women did play sport, they had to look respectable and this meant

keeping their bodies .... , which made sport ....

Many people believed that the woman's role was to stay at home and look after the

.... Thankfully things are .... now. Many sports

centres now offer ....-only sessions and .... women

are now participating in sport.

Q2 For each of the issues below, explain how women are still discriminated against.

a) Media Coverage: ....

b) Sponsorship: ....

c) Prize Money: ....

Q3 Name two sports where women can compete alongside men.

i) ....

ii) ....

Q4 List below the five main aims of the Women's Sport Foundation.

1 ....

2 ....

3 ....

4 ....

5 ....

Sporting Behaviour

Q1   Complete the sentences using words from the box below.

> back, spectator, treatment, gamesmanship, non-contact, manners,
> out the ground, team games, front, bending, violence, sportsmanship,
> fair play, injured, out of play, officials, contact

Etiquette in sport means .... In a football match, if one player is

badly ...., then the ball is normally kicked .... so

that .... can be given. When the throw-in is taken, the ball is usually

thrown .... to the team who kicked it out. In many other games, it is

good .... to shake hands with the opposition and the

.... Etiquette is often referred to as .... The

opposite of this is ...., where players try to put off their opponents by

.... the rules as much as they can get away with. However,

.... between players is still rare, especially in ....

sports. It is more common in .... and some people blame violence on

the pitch for problems with .... violence.

Q2   List two positive and two negative factors of having spectators at a sporting event.

Positive: 1 ....

2 ....

Negative: 1 ....

2 ....

Q3   Give the names and dates of the 2 stadium disasters that led to the Taylor Report.

1 ....

2 ....

Q4   List three recommendations of the report that have now
been implemented at all football league grounds.

1 ....

2 ....

3 ....

Local Sports Clubs

Q1   Write in the job that each of the following Sports Committee members does.

a) Chairperson ....

b) Vice-Chairperson ....

c) Treasurer ....

d) Secretary ....

e) Fixtures Secretary ....

f) Members Secretary ....

Q2   Draw lines to match the tasks to the correct job.

a) Administration

b) Facilities

c) Competition

d) Coaching

i)   look after the pitches/courts, changing areas, social areas and equipment

ii) encourage youngsters and help all players improve

iii) all the paperwork and organisation

iv) organising games against other clubs

Q3   Explain below how each of the following types of competition work.

a) League ....

....

b) Knock-out ....

....

c) Ladder ....

....

Sporting Facilities

Q1   Are the sports below indoor, outdoor or both? Write each one in the correct box.

i) Football   ii) Hockey   iii) Tennis   iv) Badminton   v) Cross Country

vi) Canoeing   vii) Athletics   viii) Horseracing   ix) Trampolining   x) Aerobics

Indoors	Both	Outdoors

Q2   List four factors that need to be considered when planning a sports facility.

a) ....

b) ....

c) ....

d) ....

Q3   For each of the following statements, write in PUBLIC SECTOR
or PRIVATE SECTOR to say who the facilities are run by.

a) Owned by local authorities ....

b) Run to make money ....

c) Owned by companies or individuals ....

d) Subsidised by local taxes ....

e) Includes voluntarily run facilities ....

f) Usually run at a financial loss ....

Q4   For each of the Centres of Excellence, list the sport(s) that they focus on.

a) Crystal Palace ....

b) Bisham Abbey ....

c) Lilleshall ....

d) Holme Pierrepoint ....

e) Plas-y-Brenin ....

f) National Cycling Centre ....

Sporting Bodies and Organisations

Q1 Fill in the blanks using words from the box below.

> international, nine, destroy, national, rules, pitches, four, promote, disciplined, local

Governing Bodies have .... main roles. Their main aim is to

.... their sport. This involves maintaining .... and

ensuring that those who break the rules are .... Governing Bodies also

run .... teams and organise competitions both at ....

and .... level.

Q2 Draw straight lines to match the roles performed to the correct sporting body.

a) UK Sport

i) Increase participation

ii) Support world-class performers

iii) Increase standards

iv) Improve facilities

v) Improve UK's sporting profile

vi) Provide anti-doping programme

vii) Attract major sporting events

viii) Allocate lottery funding

b) Home Country Councils

Q3 List below the four main aims of the CCPR.

a) ....

b) ....

c) ....

d) ....

Q4 List below the four main ways in which the CCPR is funded.

i) ....

ii) ....

iii) ....

iv) ....

Sporting Bodies and Organisations

Q1   Write the responsibilities under the correct organisation in the table.

i)   Organise the British Olympic team

ii)   Raise money to send the British team to the Olympics

iii)   Organise the Olympics

iv)   Decide on host city

v)   Help governing Bodies prepare athletes for the Olympics

vi)   Fight against doping and corruption

vii)   Decide on which sports to include in the Olympics

viii) Put together British bids to host the Olympics

IOC	BOA

Q2   Write out the full names for the following sports organisations.

a) NCF ....

b) SAF ....

c) CC ....

Q3   Write in below who or what the main concern of each of the sporting bodies is.

a) NCF: quality of ....

b) SAF: raising .... to help athletes who can't .... to train or compete.

c) CC : Ensuring the .... is used but also ....

Finance of Sport

Q1   Fill in the blanks using words from the box below.

> charged, match, cheese, cheap, sponsorship, subsidised, local people,
> local taxes, expensive, money, membership, parking, raffle

Public sports facilities are .... by the local

council, paid for by ....   Private sports

facilities aim to make .... and therefore are

often very .... to use.   Small sports clubs

usually cover their costs by charging .... fees

and .... fees.   A lot of voluntary clubs often

raise money through selling .... tickets or

through .... from local businesses.

Q2   What percentage of the total cost does a group have
to raise when applying for National Lottery Funding?

....

Q3   Explain below how a large media-friendly competition
and a small-scale competition are financed differently.

a) Large scale ....

b) Small scale ....

Q4   For each of the examples given below, explain how money can be raised for sport.

a) TV and Radio ....

b) Sponsorship and Merchandise ....

c) Grants ....

Sponsorship

Q1   Name five different ways sponsors put money into sport.

1 ....   4 ....

2 ....   5 ....

3 ....

Q2   Outline the benefits that the sponsors get in return for the following.

a) | Providing free clothes and equipment: | ....

....

b) | Paying large sums of money so that sporting superstars support their brand: | ....

....

....

c) | Sponsoring charity events and local events: | ....

....

d) | Universities offer scholarships (places at lower grades) to up-and-coming sports people: |

....

....

Q3   List below two types of sportspeople who would find it difficult to gain major sponsorship.

i) ....

ii) ....

Q4   Write a few short sentences below to explain why you think
       so few sports are sponsored by big tobacco or alcohol firms.

....

....

....

....

Sport and Media

Q1   List below the various types of media covering sport.

1 ....

2 ....

3 ....

4 ....

5 ....

Q2   List six different ways in which sport is represented in the media.

1 ....

2 ....

3 ....

4 ....

5 ....

6 ....

Q3   Explain how the media helps with the following issues in sport.

a) Money: ....

....

b) Education: ....

....

c) Inspiration: ....

....

d) Coaching Aid: ....

....

Q4   Identify three negative sides of the media and sport.

i) ....

ii) ....

iii) ....

<u>Amateurs and Professionals</u>

Q1   Write in below the main difference between amateur sport and professional sport.

a) Amateurs do sport for ....

b) Professionals do sport for ....

Q2   Complete the sentences below using words from the box.

> professional, impossible, CCPR, governing, fun, paid, BOA allowed, amateur, IOC

The Olympics began as a totally .... event. However, people soon

began to find ways of being .... to play sport and still compete in the

Olympics. It became .... to tell the difference between the two and so

the word .... was dropped from the Olympic rules. It is now the

.... bodies and the .... that decide who can compete.

Q3   What 3 important events happened in the amateur vs professional debate on these dates?

i) 1880 ....

ii) 1884 ....

iii) 1895 ....

Q4   Explain below the origins of the "Gentlemen and Players" cricket match.

....

....

....

....

Q5   List below four ways an amateur could earn money from sport.

i) ....

ii) ....

iii) ....

iv) ....

International Sport

Q1   Write in below how often each of the following major sporting events are held.

        a) Summer Olympics: Every ....

        b) Winter Olympics: Every ....

        c) Commonwealth Games: Every ....

        d) Pan-American Games: Every ....

Q2   Place each of the following statements about sport into the table under the correct country.

a) Sport controlled by state

b) Top college athletes drafted into professional leagues

c) Cheap sports like athletics and football are popular

d) PE is compulsory in schools

e) PE is compulsory in schools

f) Talented children trained from very early age

g) Grants available for promising talent

h) Sport has become more open since 1989

i) Top athletes often given governmental jobs

j) Some top performers have trust funds

k) Scholarship schemes help promising athletes

l) School and college sport attracts big sponsorship

m) 'Sport For All' campaigns promote participation

United Kingdom	USA	Former Eastern Bloc	Third World Countries

The Olympic Games

Q1   Complete the following sentences using words from the box below.

> facilities, terrorism, profit, expensive, tramps, hooliganism, tourists, trade, infrastructure, war, people, businesses

Being host city for the Olympics will attract .... and ....

Long after the Games have finished, the .... will still be there to be used.

During the Games, the extra amount of .... around should mean that local

.... do good trade. However, it is becoming increasingly ....

to host the Games and many poorer countries cannot afford to do so. There is also added

pressure on the city's .... (telephone system, transport etc) and a real threat

of .... or .... which could disrupt the Games. However, if

managed well, the host city should be able to make a large ....

Q2   Write in below where the following Olympics were held.

a) 1896 ....   b) 1936 ....   c) 1972 ....

d) 1980 ....   e) 1984 ....   f) 1992 ....

Q3   Draw lines to match the historical event to the host city.

a) Moscow   i)   Hitler refused to hand four gold medals to the black athlete
                          Jessie Owens (Hitler believed in Aryan supremacy)

b) Berlin   ii) South Africa participated for first time since 1964
                          (previously banned for apartheid)

c) Barcelona   iii) USA boycotted the Games over invasion of Afghanistan

d) Los Angeles   iv) First Modern Olympic Games
                          (organised by Baron de Coubertin)

e) Athens   v)   Israeli athletes killed by Palestinian terrorists

f) Munich   vi) USSR boycotted in retaliation.
                          Games made huge profit for first time.

Q4   Write a few short sentences to highlight the changes in the Olympics since they were
      reinstated until present day. Hint: Think about amateur vs professional, financing and politics.

....

....

....